PUFFIN BOOKS

Editor: Kaye Webb

The Third Big Book of Pu

Are you game for a puzzle? How do you feel about
learning to tell the time Swahili style or joining
Exploration Crackpot? Could you find out, if you
thought long enough about it, which five odd figures
add up to fourteen, and would you be able to
discover the elusive lozenge or the temple of the
Pharaoh of Tooting Common? You'd have thought
that Michael Holt and Ronald Ridout would by now
have exhausted their supplies of number puzzles,
word puzzles, jokes, tricks to play on your friends and
optical illusions, but this third collection contains
another 130 or so puzzles even more bewildering
than those contained in the first two books.
Professors Crackpot and Brainwave are back again, and
as usual Peter Edwards's illustrations provide
illumination or confusion as required. If you're
already 'hooked' on this astonishing blend of sense
and nonsense no further introduction is necessary,
but if you are approaching these puzzles unprepared,
beware! Sharpen your wits and burnish your brain
cells for another duel with the master puzzlers.

# The Third Big Book of Puzzles

By Michael Holt and Ronald Ridout

Illustrated by Peter Edwards

PUFFIN BOOKS

Puffin Books,
Penguin Books Ltd, Harmondsworth,
Middlesex, England
Penguin Books, 625 Madison Avenue,
New York, New York 10022, U.S.A.
Penguin Books Australia Ltd, Ringwood,
Victoria, Australia
Penguin Books Canada Ltd, 2801 John Street,
Markham, Ontario, Canada L 3 R 1 B 4
Penguin Books (N.Z.) Ltd, 182–190 Wairau Road,
Auckland 10, New Zealand

Published in Puffin Books 1979

Set, printed and bound in Great Britain by
Cox & Wyman Ltd, Reading
Set in Monotype Joanna

# Hints on How to Use this Book

The first *Big Book of Puzzles* was so well received that we prepared *The Second Big Book of Puzzles*. Now we have concocted yet more of the same sort of puzzles in this *The Third Big Book of Puzzles*. The mixture as before – but we have worked in some brand new puzzles, to keep you on your mental toes! The puzzles in this as in the other two books are many and various, variety being the spice of a puzzler's life: they range from those that have never seen printer's ink before to genuine old chestnuts. Something for everybody, of all ages.

We have put together three main kinds of puzzles – word puzzles, optical illusions and brain ticklers. The word puzzles include crosswords, acrostics, anagrams, hidden words in sentences, spelling bees, word meanings, riddles, and dictionary teasers. As for the optical illusions, well . . . you'll see! For seeing is believing, they say. The brain ticklers are logical and mathematical; they cover magical number tricks to try on your friends, magic squares, paper cutting, logical maps, trick questions (of course!), dice and domino puzzles and quite a few games which call for thinking rather than sheer luck. There's also a spanking new exam paper for those who like hard questions with dead easy answers.

So there are lots of different puzzles to pit your wits against. If you can't see how to solve a puzzle immediately, don't give up, will you? Put it aside and try later before you finally look up the answers, which you'll find are very fully explained, starting on page 100.

M.H.
R.R.

*We hope you have fun, again!*

# 1. On the level

Why isn't Archimedes' wall working out well?

# 2. Riddles and jokes

## Crackshot?

Did you hear about the time Professor Crackpot took a pot-shot with his gun at the sky? He aimed upwards . . . and missed.

1. What time is it when a horse sits on your fence?
2. What did the cattle do when the cowboy said 'Hi'?
3. When is a sheaf of wheat not a sheaf?
4. Three men went to sea and their boat capsized but only two got their hair wet. How was that?
5. When is a match not a match?
6. How many people can get into an empty telephone box?
7. Can you read this?

PUZZLER

## Aristotle's noses

Aristotle, the well-known (to some!) Greek philosopher, discovered how to make his one nose feel like two. You, too, can have two noses. This is what you have to do. Cross the first and second fingers of one hand. Then gently rub them along your nose, as the Professor is doing here.

# 3. In the cupboard?

The eight words needed to solve this puzzle all name bones numbered on the skeleton. Can you find them from this list?

Skull    Scapula
Ribs     Patella
Femur   Fibula
Pelvis   Spine

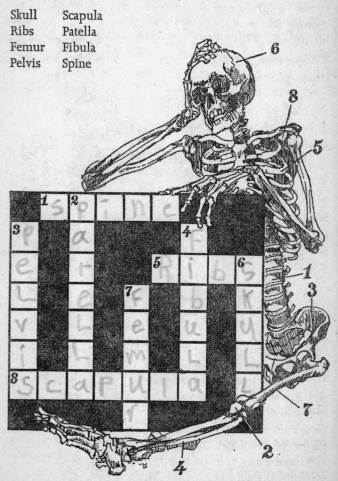

# 4. Brain baffler

The other day Professor Brainwave was designing a little picture book for Hedge, his assistant. 'Something simple and restful,' the Professor thought. We have great pleasure in showing you four pages from the 'Brainwave Picture Book for Hedgehogs', who are, as you know, colour-blind.

Hedge found these two pages nicely contrasted; as he said, 'Light grey on the left and dark grey on the right.'

But these two pages baffled his little brain. For at first sight they seemed to be a pretty pattern of greys making each side different. 'And a nice little crease down the middle to give it interest,' as he put it.

Then Hedge happened to cover the crease with a pencil. (You do the same, if you will.) 'All the interest's gone!' he squeaked. 'And with it the pattern of greys. Both sides now look alike.'

Does the pencil effect baffle your brain, too?

# 5. A proud boast

If you fill in this glidogram correctly, the second column down will form a complete and proud statement. All the words required must of course contain seven letters.

1. A drawing used to explain something
2. To sink a ship
3. The creature before it becomes a frog
4. Sad

which says I can solve it

5. The world's largest bird
6. Made from sheep's hair
7. Not allowed by law
8. Of normal standard
9. Rich
10. Success in a struggle
11. Lasting for ever

# 6. Arrows through the door

Professor Brainwave shot two arrows, one with feathers, one without, through his front door. Both arrow-heads came right through the wood. But in his efforts to pull it out, the Professor broke the head off one of the arrows.

The question is, which of the arrows, the one with feathers or the one without, belongs to the arrow-head still showing? Check it with a ruler!

# 7. Collapsible box

Here's Professor Brainwave's drawing for making a box frame. We think you'll agree, it has a front and a back linked with one connecting edge. Its great advantage, the Professor claims, is that you can pack an awful lot of things into it!

It has another advantage — so he claims.
Turn it round, like this:
and it automatically folds flat. Do you agree? The Professor says it's all in the mind.

# 8. Wasn't she kind?

Each of the words needed to solve this puzzle begins with a three-letter word. The three-letter words, when read down, form a complete question. What is the question?

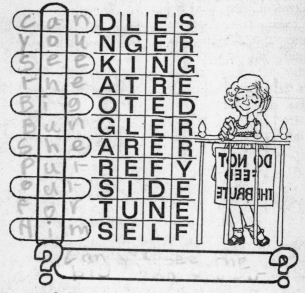

1. Wax lights
2. Less old than
3. Looking for
4. Where plays are performed
5. Narrow-minded in one's beliefs
6. He who botches what he is doing
7. He who removes the wool of sheep
8. To decompose
9. The external part
10. Wealth
11. That very man

# 9. Whiter than white

How many triangles do you see here?

Does part of the paper seem whiter than white? Cover up the black 'cheeses'. Does the whiter part now become less white? Odd, isn't it? Scientists still cannot explain this whiter than whiteness. There are many more 'seeing-is-believing' pictures in this book.

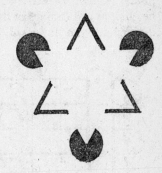

# 10. Tilt

Look at the letters of the word TILT. Are they tilted? Or do they lie on straight horizontal and vertical lines? Better check with a ruler. You may be surprised.

# 11. Where's the rest?

As you can see, the middle of each word required to solve this puzzle is itself a three-letter word. But can you find the beginnings and endings of the words? If you find them all, the first column down will spell a word meaning careful observation.

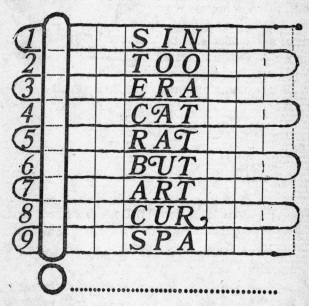

1. In an amusing way
2. Pricking the skin indelibly
3. The quality of being tolerant
4. The systematic training of the mind
5. The story line
6. A river that flows into a larger one
7. Favouring neither side
8. The state of not being widely known
9. A daily publication reporting the news

# 1 2. The Cheshire Cat

Alice had met the Cheshire Cat, who, you remember, had faded away before her very eyes. The Cheshire Cat's grin remained some time after the rest of it had gone. Here we have the opposite effect. Stare hard at the smile on the stripey cat's face ... and the smile seems gradually to fade away. Almost as curious as the Cheshire Cat's grin!

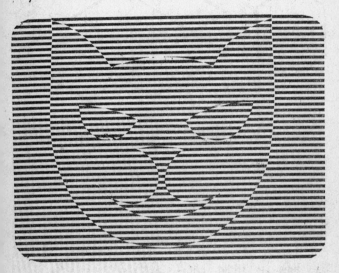

# 1 3. The fox and the grapes

Every night a fox slipped into a vineyard. Over five nights he ate sixty grapes. Each night he ate two more grapes than the night before. How many grapes did he eat the first night?

# 14. The elusive lozenge

Can you find the lozenge shown here in this picture? When you think you have found it, shade it in on the picture before looking at the answer.

# 15. The tilted lenses

The stripey pattern contains, as you can see, two round lenses, also striped. As you can also see, the stripes of one lens are tilted, compared to the stripes on the other lens . . .

Or are they? You'd better check with a ruler.

# 16. What an expression!

Can you find the missing words in these expressions? If you find them all, the third column down will make yet another expression.

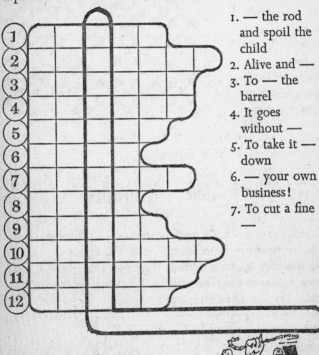

1. — the rod and spoil the child
2. Alive and —
3. To — the barrel
4. It goes without —
5. To take it — down
6. — your own business!
7. To cut a fine —

8. To beat about the —
9. On the — hand
10. To throw a — in the works
11. What are things — to?
12. To keep one's cards close to one's —

# 17. An eye-fool

What on earth can
this dotty pattern
be?
Just a jumble
perhaps? Or has
your eye been
fooled?
Hold this book at
arm's length and the
picture shows you ...

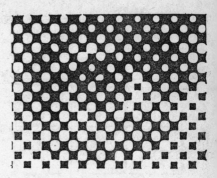

What do you think? Write it down here
and then check with the answer.

# 18. The folded silk square

Here is a square – a silk scarf for example. The problem is to
fold the square to form a smaller one half the size.
All you have to do is draw in the new square on this one,
showing where the folds will be. It's rather easier than you
think. Try it out first with a paper square.

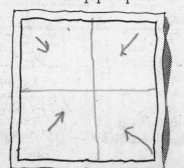

# 19. Find the circle's centre

Take a set square and pencil. Use them to find the circle's centre. Nothing else is needed.

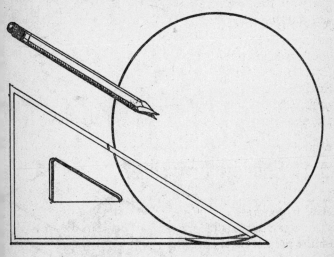

# 20. Axle trouble

The axle is longer than the wheels it connects, isn't it? The question is by how much.

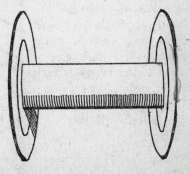

# 21. When is a tree not a tree?

Here is a tree which our artist dashed off for us.
Yet what have we here? A girl smoking a cigarette?

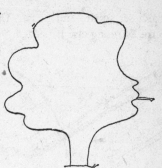

# 22. Shadow or wedge?

First it looks like a grey shadow cast by the tall block on the right of the drawing. Then it looks like a grey wedge in the block on the left. As if that were not enough of an illusion, the greyness also changes. To most people, the grey looks light grey when it is the shadow and dark grey – almost black even – when it is the wedge. Not only does the shape change: so does the colour. All very confusing.

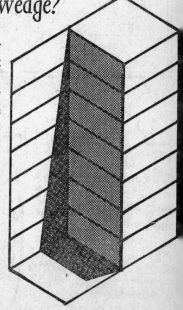

# 23. Funny sayings

Hedge asked the artist to draw pictures to illustrate some well-known sayings. But, as usual, he has got them a bit muddled up – the sayings, not the drawings! Try to guess what each muddled saying is? Don't try too hard. The clues should start you off.

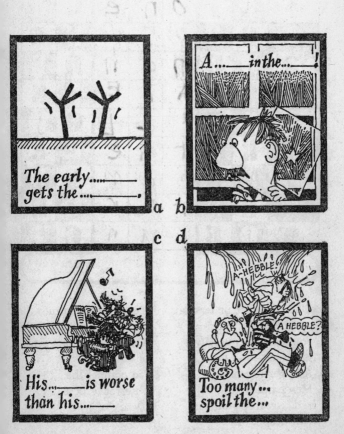

a  b

c  d

# 24. Greedy fellow!

To complete each of the words in this puzzle, you need a three-letter word. The nine three-letter words, when read down, make a complete sentence. What is it?

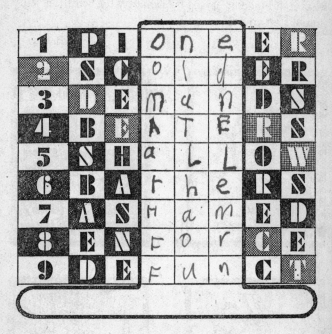

| | | | | | | |
|---|---|---|---|---|---|---|
| 1 | P | I | o | n | e | E | R |
| 2 | S | C | o | l | d | E | R |
| 3 | D | E | m | a | n | D | S |
| 4 | B | E | A | T | E | R | S |
| 5 | S | H | a | L | L | O | W |
| 6 | B | A | r | h | e | R | S |
| 7 | A | S | H | a | m | E | D |
| 8 | E | N | F | o | r | C | E |
| 9 | D | E | F | u | n | C | T |

1. One who first undertakes something
2. Someone who noisily finds fault
3. Asks for urgently
4. Men employed to drive birds towards gunmen
5. Not deep
6. People who go into the water for fun
7. Overcome with a sense of guilt
8. To compel the observance of a law
9. Dead

22

# 25. Hover bover

Here is charted the maiden voyage of Crackpot's new ecological vessel, the Hoover Bath. He wanted to go to the Isle of Wight, but thanks to its amazing laser technology it can only go in a straight line. And he missed!
Where in France did he land, Cherbourg or St Brieuc?

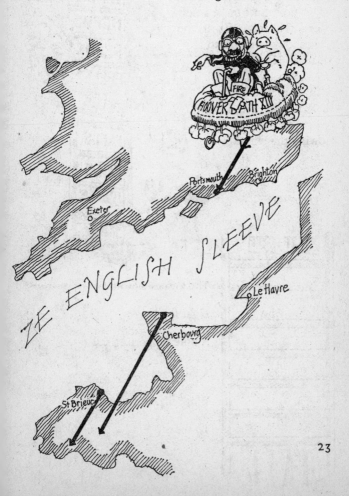

# 26. From one to another

In a laddergram you have to change one word into another. You can only change one letter at a time, and every time you change a letter you must make a new word. The example at the side shows you how to change HEADS into TAILS in seven moves. Can you now change LOST into TALL in seven moves by following the clues?

HEADS
HEEDS
FEEDS
FEELS
FELLS
FALLS
FAILS
TAILS

LOST

The greatest amount

Light fog

A pole supporting sails

A false face

Work that must be done

To speak

TALL

# 27. Draw the next shape

Can you draw the next shape in this pattern?

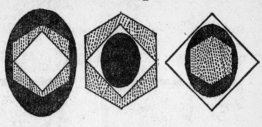

# 28. Three men's morris

This is a medieval English board game, rather like 'noughts and crosses'. Two players play it on a three-by-three board using six counters or coins – three pennies, say, and three 5p coins. They take turns at placing a coin on the board until all six coins are played. Each player aims to get

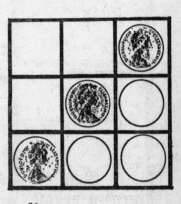

three of his own coins in a row – across, up-and-down, or on a diagonal, as in noughts and crosses. Here the 'pennies' (shaded) have won:

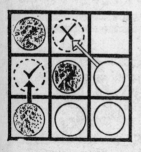

But suppose neither player reaches a winning position. They continue to play by moving a single coin of their own one square across or up-and-down (not diagonally) to an empty square.

# 29. Get ahead!

Something seems to have gone to their heads! Can you tell what it is?

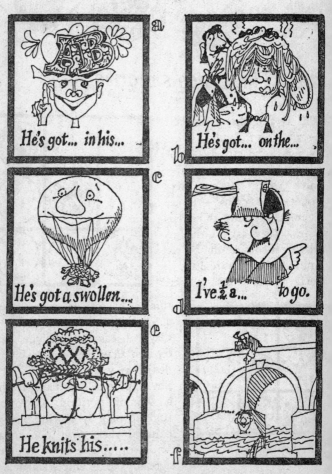

a) He's got... in his...

b) He's got... on the...

c) He's got a swollen....

d) I've ½ a... to go.

e) He knits his.....

f)

# 30. Clever of me!

All the words required to solve this glidogram have eight letters. Find them all and the second column down will tell you what you have done.

1. Without a sound
2. Moving
3. A wrecker
4. To defeat
5. Don't forget
6. To amaze
7. Able to be carried

8. Our twenty-six letters
9. To pass another car
10. A pistol
11. Good enough
12. Not plural
13. A great rush

says

# 31. A matchless puzzle

Lay out twelve matches, making four small squares and one big square, as shown in the picture.

Can you take away two matches and leave just two squares of unequal sizes?

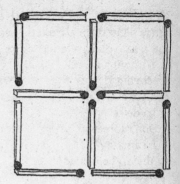

# 32. The castle moat

The matches shown here are the plan of a castle surrounded by its moat. Can you add two 'planks' – that is, matches – and get across the moat to the castle wall?

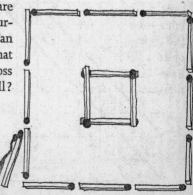

# 33. Pent-up triangles

How many triangles can you see in this pentacle, once a familiar sign of witches?

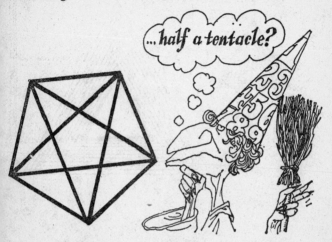

*...half a tentacle?*

# 34. Sailboat stumper

Look at the two thick lines – the sail's boom and its keel. The keel is quite a bit longer. By how much? Better measure it to find out.

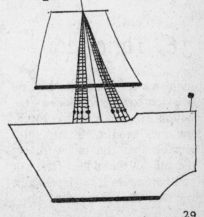

# 35. The black triangles

Which of the two thicker black triangles is the larger?

# 36. Thrice dice

In this tower of three dice there are five faces completely hidden – the bottom face and four faces touching one another. It seems incredible, but you can work out the sum of the hidden faces. All you have to do is to glance at the top face. What is the sum?

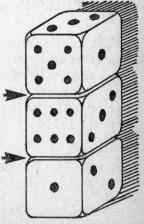

# 37. Make a nutty sandwich

There is a word hidden in the first column down, and another hidden in the last column down. The two go together to make a phrase. You can find the phrase by solving the puzzle.

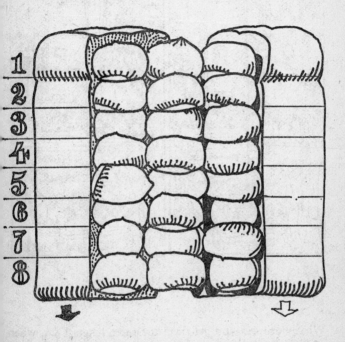

1. Once more
2. A stringed musical instrument
3. Demonstrated; explained
4. A fertile area in a desert
5. To depart
6. To do with a town or city
7. Stories
8. To get or keep out of the way of

# 38. Spot the differences

The pictures look the same but there are at least twelve differences to be found. Can you spot them?

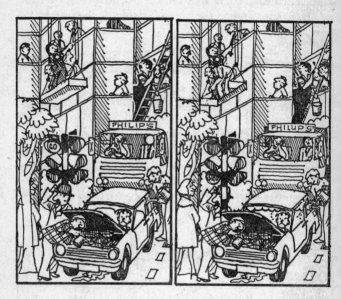

# 39. The LXR of life

What word can you get from the three letters LXR, when spoken aloud? It means a liquid that prolongs life. Stuck? Then add the vowels E, I, I.

# 40. Scrambled snapshots

Put these pictures in the order in which the events must have happened.

# 41. A glidogram

If you do this glidogram correctly, the second column down will form a complete sentence to do with this puzzle. Can you find the sentence?

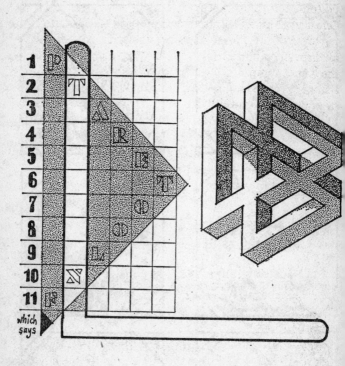

1. A trip with outdoor food
2. To try very hard
3. Few and far between
4. Not wide
5. He breathes noisily when asleep
6. Away from school
7. A fuel for cars
8. Fools
9. Courteous
10. Sufficient
11. Very weak

# 42. Millie's mix-up

In her room Millie has three shelves on which she keeps her things. On the top shelf she has put all her china and wooden horses, on the middle shelf she has all her dogs and on the bottom shelf all her vintage cars.

One day she arranged them by colour and found she had two red toys in all, two white ones, and eight blue ones, counting all three kinds, horses, dogs and cars. She also noticed she had the same number of red, white and blue dogs and the number of each was less than two. She had the same number of white dogs as white cars. Putting her blue horses and blue dogs together she found that their total came to the same as the number of blue cars.

How many of each kind and colour did Millie have? Use this grid to fill in your trial guesses and to write the totals, if you like. We've started it off for you.

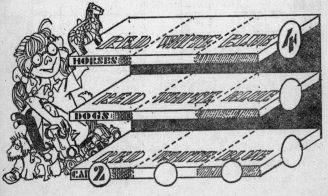

# 43. Rhyming pairs

The pair of words you have to find each time must rhyme. For example, the clue to the first word in No. 1 produces tall, while the clue to the second word produces fall. The two words rhyme.

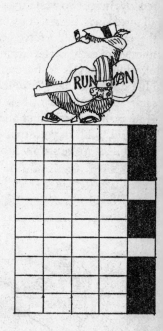

| First word | Second word |
|---|---|
| 1. High | To drop |
| 2. Just | A female horse |
| 3. A strong wind | To be unsuccessful |
| 4. To dislike | Four pairs |

| | |
|---|---|
| 5. Chief | Profit |
| 6. Expensive | In this place |
| 7. Mail | Scorched bread |
| 8. A space | A newly born horse |
| 9. A hint | Footwear |
| 10. A pain | Not genuine |

# 44. The Swahili clock puzzle

In parts of East Africa some people set their watches to
Swahili time. The Swahili day is literally the daylight hours
and runs from sunrise, 7 a.m., to sunset, 7 p.m. They call
7 a.m. the first hour or 1 o'clock. While a European's watch
shows 7 a.m., a Swahili clock will read one o'clock.

Suppose a tourist wants to have lunch at 1 p.m. What time
will it be by the Swahili clock? There is a neat trick for
changing our time into Swahili time.

# 45. Pretty patterns

The figures along each line follow a definite pattern.
What you have to do is to fill in the last figure on each line.
You fill in with shading or lines.

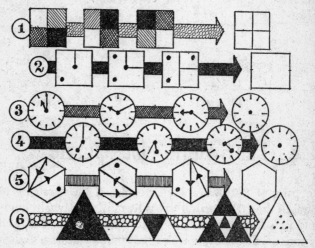

Scoring:   1 line : Mmm? Try again.        4 lines: Good.
           2 lines: Could do better.       5 lines: First rate.
           3 lines: Not bad.

# 46. Broken match squares

Take six matches and break two of them in
half. Now with the eight sticks just formed,
can you make three squares all the same
size?

# 47. Far-flung phrase

Can you find the missing words in these phrases? Check your answers with the first column down. This should make a three-word phrase meaning 'in many widely separated places'.

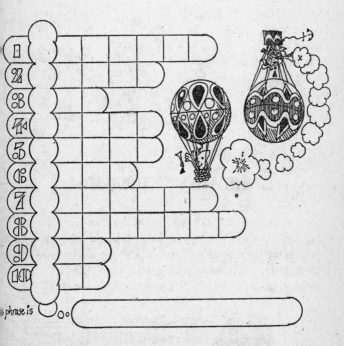

1. Fast and —
2. — of schedule
3. In the long —
4. More in sorrow than in —
5. Now or —
6. — in the mouth
7. — permitting
8. In the first —
9. Do or —
10. At the — of one's tether

# 48. Chopped cheese

Think of a ripe, round, red cheese. Cut it once with a wire cheese cutter and you have two pieces of cheese. Cut a whole cheese twice and you can get four separate pieces. Of course, if you sliced a bit off the top and bit off the bottom you'd only have three pieces, but the aim is to get the biggest number of pieces. The puzzle is: What's the most pieces you can cut a round cheese into with three clean cuts?

# 49. Brainwave's cupboard

Each autumn Mrs Brainwave makes damson jam. She stores her jars on three shelves in her cupboard. she has a neat system for keeping an eye on her jars: she always puts them so there are ten litres of jam on each shelf. The jars come in three sizes. Now can you tell how much each size is?

# 50. Rhyming answers

Each clue produces two words – the name of the thing and a word describing it. These two words rhyme. For example, the first clue produces *wild child*. To help you find the right words, a word that they both rhyme with is given alongside the clue. The ringed number shows where the first word ends and the other begins.

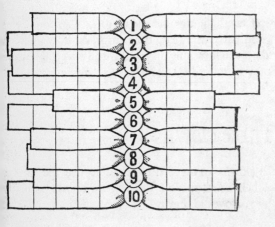

1. An untamed boy or girl (MILD)
2. Inexpensive woolly animals (KEEP)
3. A little tumble (BALL)
4. The correct illumination (KITE)
5. A plump rodent (HAT)
6. The complete dish (GOAL)
7. A moist light (CAMP)
8. Expensive drink (MERE)
9. A sluggish current (BLOW)
10. A simple profit (CHAIN)

# 51. Marbellous puzzle

Sam and Gary were totting up the marbles they each had after a game. Sam noted: 'I've got five more marbles than you've got, Gary!' Between them they had seventeen marbles. How many did each boy have?

# 52. The odd figures

Write down five odd figures that add up to 14. Can you do it? This is a good party trick. You'll be surprised how puzzled people will get and how long they will spend over this simple puzzle. But you must be careful to say 'figures' and not 'numbers'.

# 53. Three clowns

These three clowns arranged themselves so that the figures shown on their shirts made a three-figure number cleanly divisible by 7. How did they do it?

# 54. The oyster Shells

Can you tell the Walrus how many oyster shells will balance one mug?

# 55. Sam's day?

JENNIE: What day of the week is it, Sam?

SAM: Well, if tomorrow were yesterday, then today would be a Saturday.

JENNIE: You mean if today were the day before yesterday, then today would be a Saturday.

SAM: Comes to the same thing!

What day of the week was 'today'?

# 56. Find the question

Each of the words you need to solve this question is completed with a three-letter word. The nine three-letter words, when read down, form a question. Can you find it?

| # | | | | | |
|---|---|---|---|---|---|
| 1 | U N | H a | S | T Y | |
| 2 | F I | S h e | R Y | | |
| 3 | I M | P u | t E D | | |
| 4 | S H | o u | t E R | | |
| 5 | S C | h i s | M S | | |
| 6 | S C | o l d | E D | | |
| 7 | V A | c a n | C Y | | |
| 8 | A F | F o r | D S | | |
| 9 | D I | A l | C T | | |

which reads ......................................

1. Unhurried
2. The industry of catching fish
3. Attributed in a bad sense to
4. Someone who calls out loudly
5. Divisions caused by disagreement within an organization
6. Noisily found fault with
7. A post to be filled
8. Is able to spare the money for
9. A form of a language confined to a district

44

# 57. Match this!

Millie has tried lots of match tricks of a mathematical kind. But now she had thought up a couple of an unmathematical kind to stump her uncle, Professor Brainwave.

'Uncle,' she said, 'can you arrange ten matches so that they will look like ten? And when you've done that, see if you can make six matches look like nothing at all.'

Are you a match for Millie's ingenuity?

# 58. Crackpot scales

As you see, the brick balances two thirds of a brick and one third of a kilogram. Can you tell what the brick weighs?

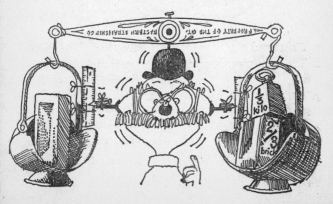

## 59. It's true

In this glidogram all the words down have eight letters. When you've found them all, the second row across will make a complete sentence telling you about the puzzle.

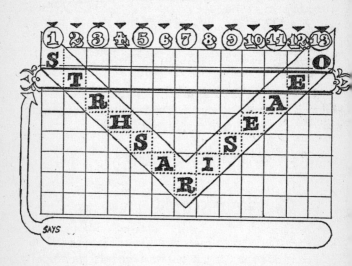

1. To make simple
2. A person who hides on board ship
3. To write hastily and carelessly
4. A man who hasn't married
5. A quickly taken photograph
6. Plentiful
7. Land used for burials
8. To surprise greatly
9. Immense
10. Without a clue
11. To empty
12. Sent back
13. Very curious people

# 60. School of Nessies

Last summer was a record one for sightings of the Loch Ness Monster. One keen local watcher claimed he saw a whole school of Nessies. He said he was near enough to see their ears.

'Two had no left ears,' he reported, 'and two had no ear flaps on the right. Two had ears on the right and two on the left. While two had both ears, two had no ear flaps at all.' The newspapers reported

TWELVE NESSIES SIGHTED

But another watcher had his camera handy and snapped the same school of Nessies. His photograph shows in black and white that there were far fewer monsters. In fact, it brings that number of monsters to the very fewest that fit the local watcher's report.

Just how many Nessies were in the school?

# 61. Single sum

Take the figures from 1 to 9, but instead of 8 use the number 0. Now make a sum:

Use our boxes. Can you write the sum with the smallest three-figure total possible with these numbers?

|   |   |   |
|---|---|---|
| 1 | 0 | 7 |
| 2 | 4 | 9 |
| 3 | 5 | 6 |

# 62. Super sum

Now take the nine figures 1 up to 9. Write a sum to get the largest three-figure total you can make out of them. Use our boxes. To start you off two are filled in.

|   |   |   |
|---|---|---|
| 2 | 3 | 5 |
| 7 | 4 | 6 |
| 9 | 8 | 1 |

# 63. The actor nephew

Uncle Ongy had come up to town to see his sister Sally Anne. He was going to take her to see the latest musical show.

'I hear it's not very good,' Sally Anne said.

'Oh, but we must see it,' Uncle Ongy said, 'my nephew Simon is in it. Only a bit part. But he's in it.'

'Well as I don't have a nephew I won't bother to come. But,' and she smiled, 'perhaps I shall come after all . . .'

What relation was Sally Anne to the mysterious nephew? So why did she change her mind?

# 64. Anagrams

Can you rearrange the letters of the word on the top of the box to make a new word – an anagram of the first – for the front of the box? As a clue, two of the letters of the new word have been put in for you.

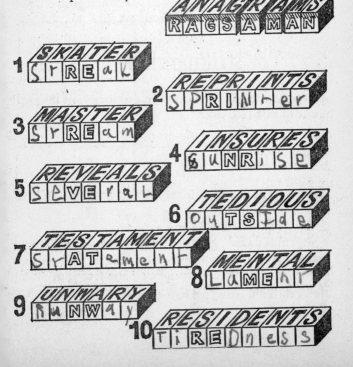

# 65. One word...

See if you can rearrange the letters of the words NEW DOOR to make one word!

# 66. Skateboards

Professor Crackpot has thirty skateboards and gives away all but two of them. How many has he got left?

# 67. The striking clock

A clock takes three seconds to strike 4 o'clock. How long will it take to strike 6 o'clock?

# 68. Round figures

'What is £11 rounded off to the nearest £10, Simple Simon?' asked Foxy Fred.

'Easy,' replied Simon, '£10.'

'Right,' said Fred. 'Now you know £11 rounded off to the nearest £20 is £20. So what is it rounded off to the nearest £100? If you get the answer right, I'll give it to you!'

How much did Foxy Fred have to give?

# 69. Strange to say

The missing words in the phrases will give you all the words to solve this puzzle. To help you find them, the meanings of the complete phrases are given alongside. Do the puzzle correctly and the first row across will produce another phrase meaning 'strange to say'.

1. In an — (immediately)
2. In the — of time (narrowly)
3. Not long — (recently)
4. Times without — (repeatedly)
5. All at — (suddenly)
6. In — silence (soundlessly)
7. Without a moment's — (instantly)
8. In the wrong — (incorrectly)
9. Up — (aloft)
10. All the — round (always)

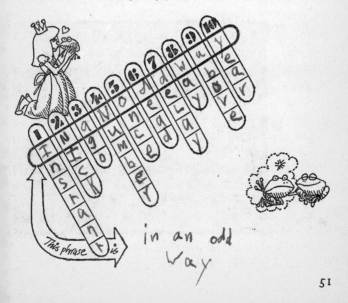

This phrase is

in an odd way

51

# 70. Pathways puzzle

How many ways can you trace, with a pencil, from the church to the house? No backtracking is allowed. And you must always use the *shortest* way.

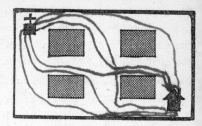

# 71. A-MAZ-ing total

There are several ways through this maze. Along each way you have to add up the numbers as you pass them. Try to pass the smallest total that you can. Can you do better than 13?

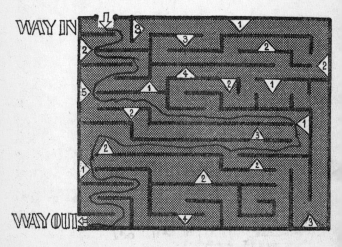

See scoring method on page 53

# 72. Do they rhyme?

The word you have to find each time must rhyme with the word given alongside the puzzle as well as satisfy the clue. If you find all the right words, the second column down will ask an appropriate question.

1. A grown-up
2. A large branch
3. Cards are this when distributed
4. The person who sees you to your seat in a theatre
5. Essential
6. Full of stones
7. To wander about stealthily
8. One's allotted portion
9. Treacle
10. Fine particles given off by something burning
11. To become completely absorbed into

**Score this way...**

YIN

The left way gives a total of (9)
The right way a total of (7)

1. RESULT
2. COW
3. KNELT
4. RUSSIA
5. TITLE
6. BONY
7. FOUL
8. PEAR
9. STIRRUP
10. CLOAK
11. URGE

IS THE QUESTION

# 73. Magic circles

A wizard had been given seven hamsters for Christmas. But he had to put them in magic circles or they would fight. First he hypnotized them so they wouldn't move. Then he put three circles round them to keep each one apart from the others.

Where did he draw his magic circles?
Draw the circles for him.

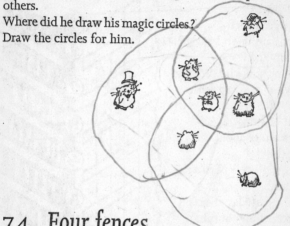

# 74. Four fences

Professor Brainwave has found some more dinosaur eggs in a square field — eleven eggs, in fact. He wants to fence them off — in case they hatch! And he wants to do so with just four straight fences. Take a pencil and draw the fences with four straight lines; the fences have to cross one another, of course.

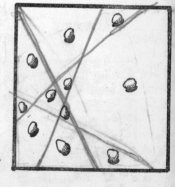

# 75. As bad as all that?

To solve this puzzle you have to find the missing word in each phrase. To help you do this, the meaning of the complete phrase is given alongside. If you find all the missing words, the third column down will give you a two-word expression suggesting you are in a desperate mood.

THIS COLUMN DOWN SAYS

1. At my own — (with me paying)
2. Out of — (inappropriate)
3. To the — (till the end)
4. — fear or favour (free from prejudice)
5. On no — (not for any reason)
6. Again and — (repeatedly)
7. By and — (on the whole)
8. Without a — in the world (friendless)
9. On the — (emphatically not)
10. At — drawn (about to fight)

# 76. Missing numbers

See if you can put in the missing number in each circle.

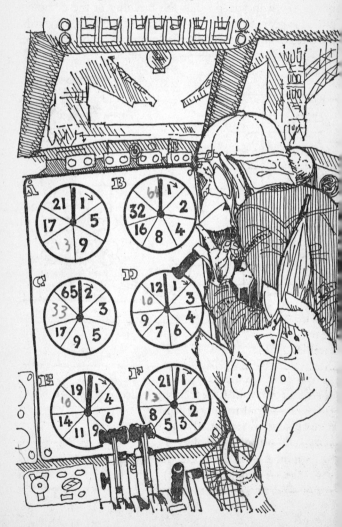

# 77. Brainwave's weighing machine

Professor Brainwave has done it again! He has designed a speak-your-weight machine – with a difference. To test it he asked his assistant Hedge to step on the platform. When Hedge did so, it said in a loud tinny voice: '2 kilograms plus half your own weight.' Hedge clicked his spines and got off, none the wiser. Can you tell how heavy Hedge is?

# 78. Quickie

Divide 50 by $\frac{1}{2}$ and add 2. What is the answer?

# 79. Fruit squash

Look at the line of letters below. Cross out six letters so that the remaining letters, without changing their order, spell out a well-known fruit.

| LSEIXMLOETTENRS |

Here's another line for you to practise on.

| LSEIXMLOETTENRS |

# 80. Opposites

You are required to find an opposite for each given word.
Each opposite has five letters and must of course begin with
the letter already in place.

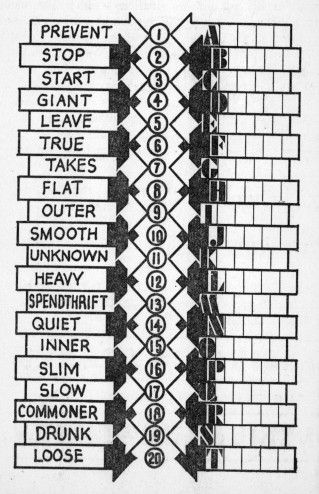

| | | | | |
|---|---|---|---|---|
| PREVENT | 1 | A | | |
| STOP | 2 | B | | |
| START | 3 | C | | |
| GIANT | 4 | D | | |
| LEAVE | 5 | E | | |
| TRUE | 6 | F | | |
| TAKES | 7 | G | | |
| FLAT | 8 | H | | |
| OUTER | 9 | I | | |
| SMOOTH | 10 | J | | |
| UNKNOWN | 11 | K | | |
| HEAVY | 12 | L | | |
| SPENDTHRIFT | 13 | M | | |
| QUIET | 14 | N | | |
| INNER | 15 | O | | |
| SLIM | 16 | P | | |
| SLOW | 17 | Q | | |
| COMMONER | 18 | R | | |
| DRUNK | 19 | S | | |
| LOOSE | 20 | T | | |

# 81. Water, gas and electricity

Here's a new twist on an old tracing problem. There are three houses, as shown, and three supplies of water (W), gas (G), and electricity (E). You've got to join up each house with mains water, gas and electricity – except one house already has a Calor gas bottle, shown with a little 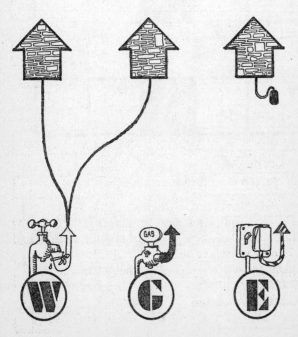, so you do not have to give it gas from the mains.
Can you draw the pipes so that no pipes cross?

We've drawn two of the water pipes for you.

# 82. A cross-number puzzle

This is like a crossword puzzle only you fill it with numbers instead of letters.

NOTE. A square number is got by multiplying a number by itself. So 169 is square because it equals 13 × 13.

*Across*

1. The next square number after 1, 4, 9, 16, 25
3. Number of days in six weeks
5. Four score and ten
6. Cards in a pack (no jokers)

7. Binary for 3
8. Make the square number from 'Snow White and the — Dwarfs'
9. Ali Baba and the — Thieves
10. 8 squared (8 × 8)

Down
2. 7×9×11 less 1
4. CCXLI in our (Arabic) numbers

6. 2 times itself nine times over, plus 2
7. The largest square number less than 200

# 83. Amused?

As you can see, all the words needed to solve this puzzle end with a three-letter word. They also begin with a three-letter word. The down column between these two sets of words spells a word showing signs of amusement.

1. The cooking room
2. A covered passage
3. Ornamented with figures
4. A schoolmaster or schoolmistress
5. The process of leaking
6. To ask or beg earnestly
7. A display case for precious things
8. An enclosed place for producing great heat
9. Performed tricks of manual skill

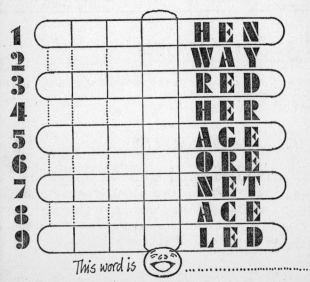

1 HEN
2 WAY
3 RED
4 HER
5 AGE
6 ORE
7 NET
8 ACE
9 LED

This word is ........................

# 84. The four fives

Professor Brainwave has written a sum on the blackboard. He was explaining to his niece Millie how to get 100 by writing just four 5s. But he has, as usual, got his signs wrong.
Can you get it right for him? You put in the signs for him.

$(5 \quad 5)(5 \quad 5) = 100$

Use one of each  $+ \quad + \quad \times$  of these signs
(Cross them off as you use them)

# 85. The four nines

Now see if you can make a 100 using four figure 9s. Can you find the trick?

# 86. The two sevens

This is rather a hard puzzle. How can you write 10 using just two 7s? To do it you need decimals. We'd better explain. The decimal 0·1 is, as you know, the same as the fraction 1/10. So 0·7 is . . . well, what? And 0·7÷7 is 0·1. That's enough of a clue for you to do the puzzle we think.

# 87. She only said 'No'

In an old British police film *The Blue Lamp* there is a scene where a detective cross-questions a little girl who might have seen the murderer. The detective tries to get her to talk. He uses charm, guile and even a bar of chocolate.

She replies sullenly and stubbornly 'No' to his every question. Finally, he says in exasperation: 'Don't you ever say anything but "no"?' Now let's suppose she was a really smart logical girl (which she wasn't, at least in the film!).

What could she have answered to be perfectly *logical*? Yes or No?

# 88. Strangers in our midst

As you can see, all the words needed to solve this puzzle begin with a three-letter word. They also end with a three-letter word. The middle column down, between these words, spells the name of unknown people.

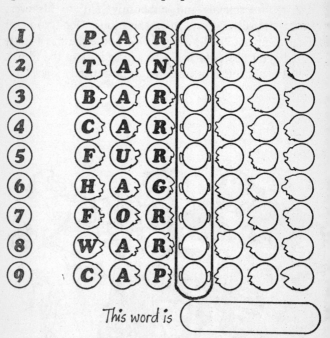

| | |
|---|---|
| (1) | P A R ◯ ◯ ◯ ◯ |
| (2) | T A N ◯ ◯ ◯ ◯ |
| (3) | B A R ◯ ◯ ◯ ◯ |
| (4) | C A R ◯ ◯ ◯ ◯ |
| (5) | F U R ◯ ◯ ◯ ◯ |
| (6) | H A G ◯ ◯ ◯ ◯ |
| (7) | F O R ◯ ◯ ◯ ◯ |
| (8) | W A R ◯ ◯ ◯ ◯ |
| (9) | C A P ◯ ◯ ◯ ◯ |

This word is ◯◯◯◯◯◯◯◯◯

1. A root vegetable
2. A ridiculous outburst of bad temper
3. A gated dam across a river
4. A house on wheels
5. A chamber in which great heat can be generated
6. Bargained about the price
7. The arm between the elbow and hand
8. To justify
9. A small winch

64

# 89. Dice with numbers

I have two dice marked with figures and not, as usual, with spots. Each of the dice, of course, is marked with the numbers 1 to 6. The two dice here show the number 24.

Now form six different two-figure numbers with the two dice, without using the same face of either dice more than once. (So you couldn't form 16 and 15, for example.)

The puzzle is this: making all these different numbers, what will they all add up to? You might think that there is more than one answer. But there isn't.

Put your numbers in the blanks here. We have given several so that you can make several shots at it.

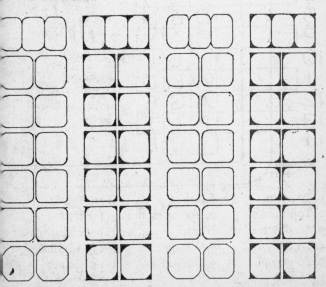

# 90. Force needed

All the six-letter words needed to solve this puzzle end, as you can see, with three-letter words. But how do they begin? If you complete all the words with the help of the brief clues, you will find that the second column down makes a polite command.

| | | | | | | |
|---|---|---|---|---|---|---|
| 1 | | | E | A | R | |
| 2 | | | H | A | S | K |
| 3 | | | A | R | K | N |
| 4 | | | T | E | N | D |
| 5 | | | E | N | D | |
| 6 | | | L | E | D | D |
| 7 | | | A | S | H | H |
| 8 | | | D | E | N | N |
| 9 | | | R | A | Y | Y |
| 10 | | | I | L | L | L |
| 11 | | | W | E | D | D |
| 12 | | | A | G | E | E |
| 13 | | | F | I | C | T |
| 14 | | | I | C | E | |

This column says:

1. To seem
2. Top marks
3. An observation
4. To fix
5. To go up
6. Cured
7. To scatter in drops
8. Abrupt
9. Into error
10. Piercing
11. Melted
12. Barbarous
13. Advantage
14. Counsel

66

# 91. The tea-table foursome

Hatter invited three of his friends to tea, Alice, Dormouse and Hare.
Hatter sits at the head of the oval table shown here.
In how many different ways can the three friends sit in the other three places? Put their initial letters in the spaces.
We have given several table layouts for you to try on.

# 92. Tangle of triangles

How many triangles are there in this figure?

## 93. Little in big

In this puzzle you have to add four letters in front of each three-letter word to make the longer word required by the clue.

1. To greet with applause
2. To stir up unrest
3. Permitted
4. The rearrangement of a word's letters to make another
5. One in addition
6. To draw to you
7. For the reason that
8. Advantage
9. A home on wheels
10. To make believe

## 94. Brainwavelets

Professor Brainwave was asked how old his youngsters Jeremy and Sarah were. 'I cannot remember, now you ask me. Hold on! I've got it . . . Take one age from the other and the answer's two; and one age "times" the other comes to 120. You should be able to work it out from that. Oh, Jeremy is the older.'

What were the two ages of the Professor's children? Put your answer here.

Jeremy was........years old. Sarah was........years old.

# 95. Exploration Crackpot

Prof. Crackpot has a team of four R2-D2 robots. With them he is planning an expedition into the unexplored Bogi Desert. They all drive desert buggies equipped with fuel tanks that hold just five gallons of super octane fuel. The buggies can go a hundred miles on a gallon. How many miles did the Professor go in the desert? His buggy carried more than enough food and water for him.

CLUE: He could syphon off fuel from the robots' buggies which just conked out when they ran out of fuel.

# 96. The lone litre

Out camping, Prof. Brainwave found he had only a three-litre and a five-litre can. He wanted exactly one litre of water for cooking. How did he measure out one litre from the river near by?

# 97. Down the ladder

This is another laddergram (see puzzle 26). You have to change FOOL into COAX. This time there are pictures for clues. Each new word you make must spell the name of one of the objects pictured.

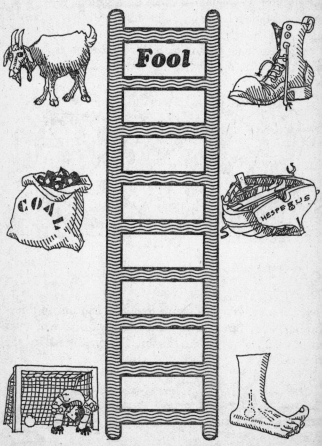

# 98. The plot of grass

A farmer wanted to fence off a plot of grass for grazing his sheep. The landowner said he could have as much land as he could fence off, with a long electric wire. BUT he must make the wire touch each of the four plum trees, shown below, and the wire must form just three straight lines.

Can you draw the three straight lines to touch each of the trees here? Your third line must return to where you started from.

# 99. The leaping frogs

Jermin, Kermin and Lermin are three highly trained frogs. They line up on a hop scotch strip like this:

As you see, there is an empty square on the left. They hop forward and back (into an empty square) and leap-frog over one another (provided there's an empty square to land in). And they end up in reverse order, like this:

With the empty square still on the left.

They manage it in five moves.

The puzzle is: How do they do it?

Put their moves down on this blank grid.

| Begin | | | |
|---|---|---|---|
| 1 | | | |
| 2 | | | |
| 3 | | | |
| 4 | | | |
| 5 | | | |

72

# 100. They rhyme

You can check your solution to this puzzle since the words have to rhyme. The first and second words rhyme, the third and fourth, and so on.

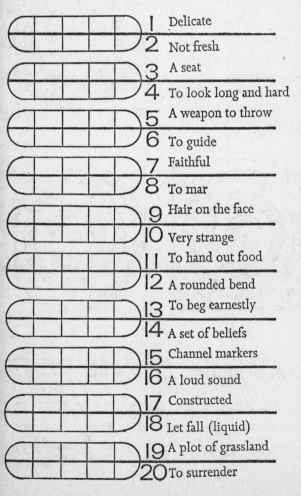

| | |
|---|---|
| 1 | Delicate |
| 2 | Not fresh |
| 3 | A seat |
| 4 | To look long and hard |
| 5 | A weapon to throw |
| 6 | To guide |
| 7 | Faithful |
| 8 | To mar |
| 9 | Hair on the face |
| 10 | Very strange |
| 11 | To hand out food |
| 12 | A rounded bend |
| 13 | To beg earnestly |
| 14 | A set of beliefs |
| 15 | Channel markers |
| 16 | A loud sound |
| 17 | Constructed |
| 18 | Let fall (liquid) |
| 19 | A plot of grassland |
| 20 | To surrender |

# 101. Sharp-shooting

Here is a target for you to hit with your pencil.

You have to score 96 with six shots – but you must land your shots in pairs – two in each ring. So if you hit the 20 ring, you must put another shot in that ring.

The scores for each ring are shown on the first target; the others are for your practice shots.

# 102. Months of the year

How many months have twenty-eight days in them?

74

# 103. Half the area

Take twelve matches and put them in the shape of a triangle like this one; its sides, as you see, are 3, 4 and 5 matches long. We have drawn them on a grid, where each grid square is a 'match square'. You can see that the triangle encloses an area of six grid squares. If you are not sure about this, check that the grid itself covers $3 \times 4$ or twelve squares. So the triangle shuts in half of this, or six squares.

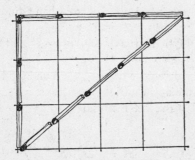

Now move four matches to make a shape that shuts in half the area of the triangle.

# 104. Shifty eyed

Crackpot has mislaid his glasses again. He looks to the left for them, he looks to the right. He looks both ways, doesn't he? Look closer at the picture and see.

# 105. Conundrums

How many of Prof. Crackpot's riddles can you guess?
1. Why does a giraffe eat so little?
2. One of Millie's hens once laid an egg that was 10 m long. Can you beat it?
3. Three fat women were walking under a tiny umbrella. Why didn't any of them get wet?
4. Why do we buy clothes?
5. Why is an empty matchbox better than a full one?
6. What has 100 legs but cannot walk?
7. Where will Prof. Brainwave's cat always be when the light goes out?
8. What is the difference between a hill and a pill?
9. What did the north wall say to the west wall?
10. Why did Millie lose her head?

# 106. Deuced dice

One evening Professor Brainwave sat down to a leisurely game of ludo with his niece Millie. After they'd been playing a little Millie suddenly said: 'Uncle, I seem to throw lots of double fours, double fives and so forth.'

'Aren't you lucky,' sighed the puzzled Professor, 'I never seem to get a double six, but, like you, I get plenty of the other deuced doubles, drat it.'

How many different doubles can you throw with two dice? Put them on the blank faces of the dice shown here.

# 107. Sales stunt

In sales you often see reductions like

and

Think of a price – double figures will be enough.
Write it here:

Now work out 10% of your price.
Put it here:

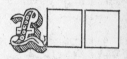

Remember, 10% of a price is a tenth of it.

Now work out 10% off your price.
That is, your price less a tenth of it.
Put the result here:

Now add this last result (10% off) to your first result (10% of).
And the answer is your price! Right?

Try it again with another price. Of course, it doesn't have to be a price. You could try it on a friend by asking him to think of a number.

# 108. Tricky tusk

Which piece of ivory is reduced in price?

# 109. Look, no remainder!

This is a bet we are making with you. Write the numbers 1 to 9 in any order you like. Put your nine-figure number in the space below. Now divide it by 9; we bet you that there will be no remainder. We have put one such number in for you.

9 ) | 4 | 7 | 8 | 6 | 5 | 2 | 1 | 9 | 3 |

9 ) |   |   |   |   |   |   |   |   |   |

9 ) |   |   |   |   |   |   |   |   |   |

9 ) |   |   |   |   |   |   |   |   |   |

A good way to do this is to ask a friend to pick nine cards, ace up to nine. Put them in any order to make a nine-figure number. You bet him that his number will divide exactly by 9.

You can also use this puzzle as a party trick. Try it on your friends.

# 110. A number jig

In this puzzle – called a number jig – numbers have to be fitted in the blanks. To start you off, one of the four figure numbers, 4400, has already been entered.

| 5 figures | 3 figures | 2 figures |
|-----------|-----------|-----------|
| 23456     | 580       | 61        |
| 27559     | 234       | 12        |
| 51023     | 275       |           |
|           | 891       |           |
| 4 figures | 407       |           |
| 4400      | 993       |           |
| 8188      |           |           |
| 2220      |           |           |

# 111. Test your word power

Which gives the right answer? Write the letter in the grid below. If you pick all the right answers, the letters in the grid will make a two-word command.

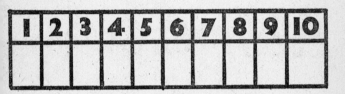

| 1 | 2 | 3 | 4 | 5 | 6 | 7 | 8 | 9 | 10 |
|---|---|---|---|---|---|---|---|---|----|
|   |   |   |   |   |   |   |   |   |    |

1. A colt is (b) a young female horse (c) a young male horse (d) any young horse
2. In a leap year there are (h) 366 days (i) 365 days (j) 364 days
3. A floe is (m) a small chimney (n) running water (o) a sheet of floating ice
4. The prow of a ship is found (n) at the rear (o) in the front (p) on the right
5. Incoherent speech is (q) easy to follow (r) dishonest (s) disconnected
6. A cleaver is used by (d) a gardener (e) a butcher (f) a blacksmith
7. The femur is (w) the thigh bone (x) the knee bone (y) the shin bone
8. An octogenarian is (e) in his eighties (f) in his sixties (g) less than eighty
9. All vertebrate animals have (j) four legs (k) wings (l) a spinal column
10. From uranium it is possible to produce (l) atomic energy (m) brass (n) petrol

# 112. Loopy sums

Can you put one of the numbers 0, 1, 2, 3, 4 and 5 in each disc so that each loop of four numbers adds up to 10? We've already put in zero and 1 for you.

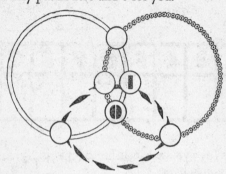

# 113. Catherine wheel

A catherine wheel has eight spokes each with its own firework on it. How many spaces are there between spokes? Draw it here.

# 114. The hopping rabbits

Here are four clever rabbits, numbered 1, 2, 3, 4. They have been trained to reverse their order, so they finish up 4, 3, 2, 1. Each can hop to the next square (if it's empty) or leap over another rabbit to a square, if free: they move just as you do in draughts. They can go or hop backwards and forwards. How do they reverse their order? They can do it in ten moves. Put your moves down on the grid provided.

# 115. Anagrams plus

These are anagrams with a difference. You have to make the new word from the letters of the starter plus an added letter. You are given a clue to the new word below. The first answer has been written in for you.

1. Already put into gear
2. A little river
3. Removes the dirt
4. A polite way of saying women
5. A surface on which films are projected

6. To mend
7. Maps for navigating
8. The opposite of junior
9. A flower arrangement given in memory
10. Bold or audacious

| | Starter | and | New Word | | | | | |
|---|---------|-----|---|---|---|---|---|---|
| 1 | Grade | E | G | E | A | R | E | D |
| 2 | Terms | A | | | | | | |
| 3 | Scale | N | | | | | | |
| 4 | Ideal | S | | | | | | |
| 5 | Sneer | C | | | | | | |
| 6 | Riper | A | | | | | | |
| 7 | Trash | C | | | | | | |
| 8 | Rinse | O | | | | | | |
| 9 | Heart | W | | | | | | |
| 10 | Grand | I | | | | | | |

# 11 6. Half full or half empty?

Professor Brainwave had gone to dinner with Professor Crackpot. Crackpot served the wine in tall glasses. 'So's you can see we both get the same,' he chuckled, 'they are perfect cylinders or tubes.'

As they drank their wine, they talked about this and that. Professor Brainwave put his glass of wine down and declared 'Good grief. Mine's over half empty already.'

'No it's not,' said Crackpot. 'It's a little over half full.'

How could the two geniuses tell without using string, ruler, or other measurers – or tipping out the wine – if his glass was just about half full or half empty?

# 11 7. The hats mix-up

The last three guests were leaving Professor Crackpot's fancy-dress party. Everyone was very merry. The three guests took their hats and their leave.

Mr Green had come in a green beret, Mr Black in a black homburg and Mr White in a white bowler.

As they said 'Good night' the good Professor noticed that none of them was wearing his own hat. 'What a mix-up!' he muttered happily to himself.

How many ways can a hat mix-up like this happen?

# 118. The '15-puzzle' magic square

You know the '15 puzzle'? It's the one where you have fifteen movable blocks, numbered 1 to 15. They are arranged in a 4×4 tray in counting order, but with the 14 and 15 reversed, as shown here. The puzzle is to shift them about till the 14 and 15 are in the proper order.

The space is for shifting the blocks around in. Now we won't ask you to solve *that* famous puzzle, already over a century old. Unless you resort to such tricks as turning the 6 and the 9 blocks upside down, that puzzle is impossible to solve.

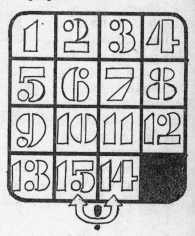

Our puzzle is simpler and can be solved. Make a '*magic*' *square* out of the fifteen numbers so they add up to 30 along each row and each column and the two diagonals. We have put in a few numbers and the blank to help you.

Practice squares:

# 119. Word endings

Each of the six-letter words required to complete this puzzle ends in a three-letter word. You are given the list of three-letter words to choose from. Can you put them in their right places to make the fifteen longer words?

| # | | | | | | | | | |
|---|---|---|---|---|---|---|---|---|---|
| 1 | I | M | P | | | | H | E | R |
| 2 | L | A | T | | | | R | E | D |
| 3 | B | U | T | | | | S | O | N |
| 4 | F | A | S | | | | A | C | T |
| 5 | A | S | L | | | | T | O | N |
| 6 | B | E | L | | | | F | R | Y |
| 7 | S | P | L | | | | L | E | D |
| 8 | S | U | D | | | | I | L | L |
| 9 | A | S | T | | | | A | G | E |
| 10 | S | H | R | | | | A | N | T |
| 11 | S | A | V | | | | T | E | N |
| 12 | P | R | I | | | | A | S | H |
| 13 | N | A | R | | | | R | A | Y |
| 14 | A | D | D | | | | R | O | W |
| 15 | S | H | A | | | | D | E | N |

## Don't answer questions you can't answer.

**o.** Elucidate the following

$\quad$ **a** $\frac{1}{3} + \frac{1}{3} = \frac{2}{3}$ $\quad$ **b** $\frac{1}{2} + \frac{1}{2} = 1$ $\quad$ **c** = please yourself!

**1.** Subcontract the following (polite) expressions:

$\quad$ **a** $7 - 3 =$ $\quad$ **b** $10 - 10 =$ $\quad$ **c** $1\frac{1}{2} - 1 =$

**2.** Adumbrate these quanta:

$\quad$ **a** $1 + 2 + 3 =$ $\quad$ **b** $10$ cm ? (near enough)

$\quad\quad\quad$ **c** £$100$ + \$$100 =$

**3.** Find the value of: **a** $- 3 + 3 =$ $\quad$ **b** $0 =$ $\quad$ **c** $! =$
What do you notice about your answers –
(*a*) anything or (*b*) nothing?

**4.** Sketch an iso-cube (or an ice-cube) (*a*) in aero-
plane (plane) (*b*) in escalation. How many faces
has it got? Marks will be given for nearness.
Is a sheet of paper two-faced? (Or are you?)

**5.** Escalate the following:

$\quad$ **a** $5 + 5 =$ $\quad$ **b** $3 \times 7 =$

$\quad$ **c** $10 + 2 =$ $\quad$ **d** $20 + 10 =$

In which parts did you use division?
In which parts did you use multiplicity?

*Don't hurry, the numbers will wait —*

# 120. Bird-brain teasers

Professor Brainwave has been hard at work devising a new
exam paper for those who like hard questions but easy
answers. At enormous expense he hired Dr Bird to help him.
After much heart-searching and then re-searching they have
come up with a really new maths exam paper. They have
called the questions 'Bird-brain teasers'. Hedge thinks
there's something funny about that title. Hedge has a word
of advice – if you don't like it, you can always pass it on!

**6.** Study the angles in the figure. Use them to dissolve angle B. Give the angles pretty names.

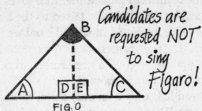

*Candidates are requested NOT to sing Figaro!*

FIG. O

**7.** Put the numbers in set S into two sets — fractions and neutral numbers:

$$S = \{1, \tfrac{1}{2}, 4, \tfrac{3}{4}, 5, \tfrac{2}{3}, 1/5\}$$

P.S.

*If you can't understand this, you are in good company —* Hedge

**8.** Use Mendel's arithmetic (or your own) to express — don't rush! — in the sanest terms:

**a** =    **b** $5$ =    **c** $\tfrac{1}{2} + 1$ =

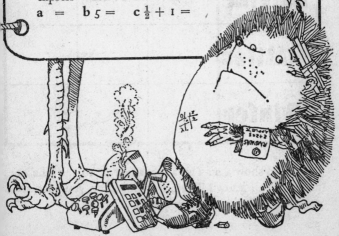

# 1 2 1. The three jobs

Professor Brainwave took Millie, who loves horses, to Camborne Stables. While Millie talked to the horses, Brainwave became more interested in what the trainer, jockey and head lad earned. Their names were Winter, Miles and Smythe though Brainwave couldn't remember who was which. But he learnt these things about them.

The head lad, who is an only child, earns the least money of all three. Miles, who married Winter's sister, earns more than the jockey.

Can you tell who has which job? It will help to fill in the table.

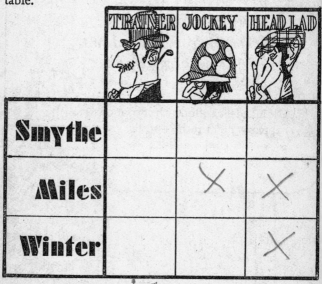

| | TRAINER | JOCKEY | HEAD LAD |
|---|---|---|---|
| **Smythe** | | | |
| **Miles** | | X | X |
| **Winter** | | | X |

Put a ✓ to show a man *has* a job, and a ✗ to show he does not. So if you know Miles is not the jockey, you put a cross opposite 'Miles' and under 'jockey'.

# 122. Add a word to make a word

Can you make ten longer words by adding the right three-letter words from the blackboard? Do so correctly and the first column down will give you two words telling you whose travelling bags they are.

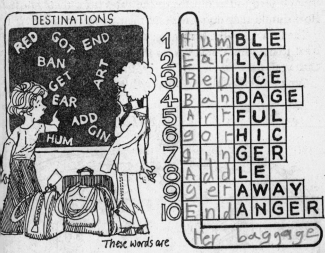

DESTINATIONS

RED  GOT  END
BAN      ART
GET
EAR
     ADD  GIN
HUM

1. HumBLE
2. EarLY
3. ReDUCE
4. BanDAGE
5. ArtFUL
6. gotHIC
7. ginGER
8. AddLE
9. earAWAY
10. EndANGER

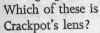

These words are

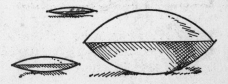

Her baggage

# 123. Raise your glasses

Crackpot bumped into Brainwave the other day. Both had lost a lens from their glasses. Crackpot is short-sighted, Brainwave is long-sighted, so Crackpot's lens is more sharply curved. Which of these is Crackpot's lens?

# 124. The quarrelsome neighbours

Mr A built two houses on his patch of land and sold them to Mr B and Miss C, as shown on the plan below. Note: Mr A's house is joined to the fence. As you see, the patch has three gates. Every time the neighbours met, they quarrelled. So they decided to build paths to the gates from their houses. How should they do so without their paths crossing? Mr A insisted on using the bottom gate, a. Just to be awkward, Mr B has to use gate b and Miss C agreed to use gate c.

Can you draw their paths for them? Remember, they mustn't cross – or their owners will get cross!

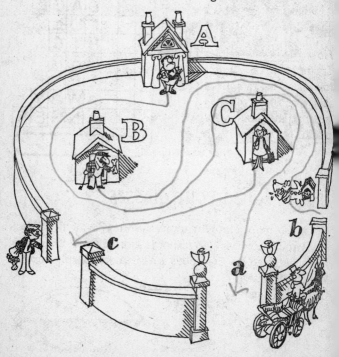

# 125. Fair squares

Professor Brainwave was trying to draw a square on a clean sheet of paper. But once again he'd lost his glasses – actually they were perched on his forehead! – and so he couldn't read the markings on his nice new ruler.

'Good grief,' he sighed to his assistant Hedge. 'What am I to do? I don't mind what size the square is. Well, just so long as it fits on the page.'

Hedge couldn't read the ruler either but he suggested: 'I know, Prof., why don't you use the corner of the page in some way?'

'Brainwave, Hedge!' said the Prof. But he was not talking about himself.

How did Professor Brainwave draw his square? Draw yours in the space below. Use a pencil and ruler but you mustn't use the markings on it!

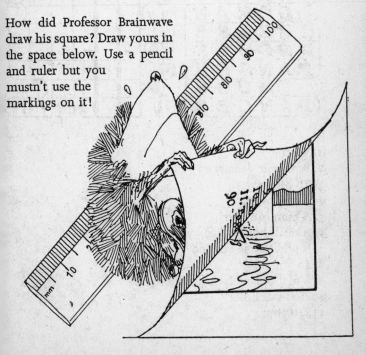

# 126. In a new guise

Each word required to solve this puzzle is made up of the letters in the given word. It is an anagram. You are given clues to the meanings of the anagrams below. You will find an extra clue in the second column down. This forms two words very relevant to the puzzle.

| Given word | No. | Answer (handwritten) |
|---|---|---|
| SCARE | 1 | cares |
| PLUMS | 2 | slump |
| GOLF | 3 | flog |
| LEAN | 4 | lane |
| RENTAL | 5 | antler |
| OCEAN | 6 | canoe |
| GREASE | 7 | agrees |
| ROGUES | 8 | grouse |
| DANGER | 9 | garden |
| MUGS | 10 | smug |
| DANCES | 11 | ascend |

*all angrams* (handwritten)

1. Worries
2. Economic depression
3. To beat severely
4. A narrow road
5. A horn of a deer
6. A small boat moved by paddles
7. Is of the same opinion
8. To grumble
9. A plot of land for cultivation
10. Self-satisfied
11. To go up

# 127. Ancient wonder

Professor Crackpot claims to have excavated the plug-hole of the lost Valley of Kings, uncovering, he says, this Temple of Pharaoh Tooting Common, one of the ancient wonders of the world. Why not colour it in?

# 1 28. Chinese plate-spinner

The Chinese plate-spinner is using a thick bamboo pole to balance his spinning plate. Can he keep it up? The pole is longer than the plate is wide, you note. Or is it?

# 1 29. Potty proverb

A king who lived a long time ago in the jungle was given a gold throne to sit on. So worried was he, however, that someone might steal it, that he never sat on it but stowed it away in the roof of his grass house. Then one night, as he slept soundly beneath his precious throne, it fell down and brained him.

Moral: People who live in grass houses Can you complete the proverb?

# 130. De-composition

Could you tell a portrait of a well-known composer if you saw it? Here are two.
Can you work out the others?

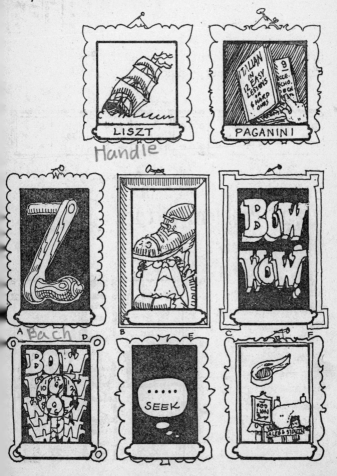

# 131. Domino fractions

This pair of dominoes can be looked at as a pair of fractions $\frac{5}{6} + \frac{1}{6} = \frac{6}{6} = 1$

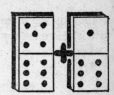

so they add up to 1.

Can you find other pairs that add up to 1?
Can you make the four dominoes add up to 2?

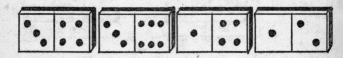

# 132. Problem picture

What could this be a picture of?

# 133. Cheerio!

With this puzzle we sign ourselves off, hoping to meet you again in the next Big Book of Puzzles.

1. Friendly
2. Feeling no shame about it
3. Equidistant for their whole length
4. Persons living together in one house
5. Skill or cleverness
6. A coloured silk handkerchief with spots
7. Containing subtle sarcasm
8. The study of armorial bearings
9. In an elaborately ornamented way
10. A blow that finishes a boxer

# Answers

## 1. ON THE LEVEL
Although the horizontal lines look wonky, they are perfectly straight.

## 2. RIDDLES AND JOKES
1. Time to get a new fence.
2. Low. (Cattle low, don't they?)
3. When it's awry.
4. One of them was bald.
5. When it's aflame.
6. None, because otherwise it isn't empty.
7. PUZZLED. Lay a card over the top half of the figures, which is a mirror image of the lower half.

### Aristotle's Noses
The reason is that you are using the insides of your fingers as if they were the outsides. This gives a wrong mental picture about the position of your fingers. So your mind tells you you are touching not one but two noses – one for each 'unusual' side of each finger.

## 3. IN THE CUPBOARD?

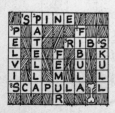

# 5. A PROUD BOAST

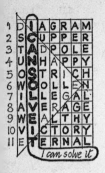

1 D (I)AGRAM
2 S (C)UPPER
3 T (A)DPOLE
4 U (N)HAPPY
5 O (S)TRICH
6 W (O)OLLEN
7 I (L)LEGAL
8 A (V)ERAGE
9 W (E)ALTHY
10 V (I)CTORY
11 E (T)ERNAL

*I can solve it*

# 8. WASN'T SHE KIND?

1 (CAN)DLES
2 (YOU)NGER
3 (SEE)KING
4 (THE)ATRE
5 (BIG)OTED
6 (BUN)GLER
7 (SHE)ARER
8 (PUT)REFY
9 (OUT)SIDE
10 (FOR)TUNE
11 (HIM)SELF

*Can you see the big bun she put out for him?*

# 11. WHERE'S THE REST?

1 (A)MUSINGLY
2 (T)ATTOOING
3 (T)OLERANCE
4 (E)DUCATION
5 (N)ARRATIVE
6 (T)RIBUTARY
7 (I)MPARTIAL
8 (O)BSCURITY
9 (N)EWSPAPER

*Attention*

## 13. THE FOX AND THE GRAPES

On the first night he ate 8 grapes. Work it out by trial and error. Or use algebra, like this: first night's meal is $g$ grapes.

So $60 = g + g + 2 + g + 4 + g + 6 + g + 8$ or $60 = 5g + 20$

So $5g = 40$ or $g = 8$, the number of grapes he ate on the first night.

## 14. THE ELUSIVE LOZENGE

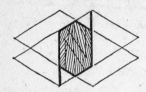

## 15. THE TILTED LENSES

Actually the stripes on both lenses are parallel and vertical. The surrounding pattern of stripes makes them look tilted to one another.

## 16. WHAT AN EXPRESSION!

1. SPARE
2. KICKING
3. SCRAPE
4. SAYING
5. LYING
6. MIND
7. FIGURE
8. BUSH
9. OTHER
10. SPANNER
11. COMING
12. CHEST

A crying shame

## 17. AN EYE-FOOL

An eye.

## 18. THE FOLDED SILK SQUARE

Fold the corners in, as shown, to form the square shown inside —
which is half the size of the original silk square.

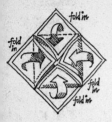

## 19. FIND THE CIRCLE'S CENTRE

Lay the set square with the right angle on the circle. Mark where its
two shorter sides cut the circle. Join these marks with a line. Do this
again after turning the set square through about a quarter turn.
The centre will be the point where the two lines cross.

## 20. AXLE TROUBLE

The axle is the same length as the diameter of each wheel.

## 23. FUNNY SAYINGS

The early worm gets the bird.
A pane in the neck.
His bark (Bach) is worse than his bite.
Too many brooks spoil the cough.

## 24. GREEDY FELLOW!

One old man ate all the ham for fun.

## 25. HOVER BOVER

St Brieuc. Try a ruler!

## 26. FROM ONE TO ANOTHER

## 27. DRAW THE NEXT SHAPE

It is the same as the first shape on the left.

## 29. GET AHEAD!

He's got a bee in his bonnet.
He's got food on the brain.
He's got a swollen head.
I've half a mind to go.
He knits his brows.
He's keeping his head above water.

## 30. CLEVER OF ME!

## 31. A MATCHLESS PUZZLE

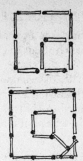

## 32. THE CASTLE MOAT

## 33. PENT-UP TRIANGLES

Thirty-five.

## 34. SAILBOAT STUMPER

The boom and the keel are the same length.

## 35. THE BLACK TRIANGLES

They are both the same size.

## 36. THRICE DICE

Opposite faces of a die add up to 7. So the top face and the five hidden faces add up to 21. Take away the top face (3) to give the answer 18.

## 37. MAKE A NUTTY SANDWICH

|   | A | G | N |
|---|---|---|---|
| 1 | B | A | O |
| 2 | S | N | N |
| 3 | O | H | S |
| 4 | L | A | E |
| 5 | U | E | N |
| 6 | T | R | S |
| 7 | E | A | E |
| 8 |   | V | S |

Absolute nonsense

## 38. SPOT THE DIFFERENCES

The woman is in front of the tree, the man behind the traffic light, which has changed. The men on the cradle have changed position, and so has the cradle, and the men are pulling on the office worker's tie. The window cleaner is on the other side of the ladder. He is cleaning faces, and his bucket is turned. Philip's lorry has changed to Phillips' and now has a back. The driver's mate has a face instead of a blank. And the car is full of water.

## 39. THE LXR OF LIFE

Elixir.

## 40. SCRAMBLED SNAPSHOTS

e, c, d, f, a, b.

## 41. A GLIDOGRAM

## 42. MILLIE'S MIX-UP

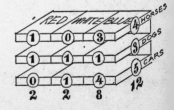

## 43. RHYMING PAIRS

| | | |
|---|---|---|
| 1 | TALL | FALL |
| 2 | FAIR | MARE |
| 3 | GALE | FAIL |
| 4 | HATE | EIGHT |
| 5 | MAIN | GAIN |
| 6 | DEAR | HERE |
| 7 | POST | TOAST |
| 8 | HOLE | FOAL |
| 9 | CLUE | SHOE |
| 10 | ACHE | FAKE |

## 44. THE SWAHILI CLOCK PUZZLE

Seven o'clock, Swahili time. The trick is to follow the hour hand back and see where it points. When the hour hand points to 7, its 'tail' (if it had one) points to 1.

## 45. PRETTY PATTERNS

  1       2       3       4       5       6

## 46. BROKEN MATCH SQUARES

| | |
|---|---|
| 1 | FURIOUS |
| 2 | AHEAD |
| 3 | RUN |
| 4 | ANGER |
| 5 | NEVER |
| 6 | DOWN |
| 7 | WEATHER |
| 8 | INSTANCE |
| 9 | DIE |
| 10 | END |

Far and wide

## 47. FAR-FLUNG PHRASE

## 48. CHOPPED CHEESE

Eight pieces. Imagine making one cut vertically, like a wall in a room, another vertically like a wall at right-angles to the first, then the third cut horizontally, to form a 'floor' across the middle of the cheese. Then you have four 'rooms' upstairs, and four 'rooms' downstairs – or eight 'rooms' in all: that's eight pieces of cheese.

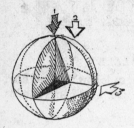

## 49. BRAINWAVE'S CUPBOARD

Take away four little jars from the bottom two shelves and you know that one big jar holds as much jam as two medium jars. Take away one big jar and one little jar from the top two shelves and you know one medium jar holds as much jam as three little jars – and so one big jar (= two medium jars) holds the same as six little jars. The bottom shelf tells you that two medium jars (= six little jars) and four little jars hold ten litres; that is, ten little jars hold ten litres. So each little jar holds one litre; then a medium jar holds three litres and a big jar holds six litres.

## 50. RHYMING ANSWERS

## 51. MARBELLOUS PUZZLE

Gary had six marbles and Sam eleven.

## 52. THE ODD FIGURES

We said figures. Here they are, five 1s, adding up to 14.

```
    11
     1
     1
  + 1
  ───
    14
```

## 53. THREE CLOWNS

The clown with 6 stood on his hands; and then they made 931, which divided by 7 is 133.

## 54. THE OYSTER SHELLS

A bottle and two mugs balance nine shells.
But a bottle balances five shells.
So two mugs balance four shells, and each mug balances two shells.

## 55. SAM'S DAY?

Monday. Sam and Jennie are both saying if it were two days earlier it would be Saturday; so two days forward must be Monday.

## 56. FIND THE QUESTION

```
1 UN HAS TY
2 FI SHE RY
3 IM PUT ED
4 SH OUT ER
5 SC HIS MS
6 SC OLD ED
7 VA CAN CY
8 AF FOR DS
9 DI ALE CT
```

(?) Has she put out his old can for ale?

## 57. MATCH THIS!

Arrange the nine matches to spell the word TEN. Then make the six matches spell NIX.

## 58. CRACKPOT SCALES

The missing third of the broken brick is made up in weight by the $\frac{1}{3}$ kilogram. So a third of a brick weighs $\frac{1}{3}$ kilogram. That is, a brick weighs 1 kilogram.

## 59. IT'S TRUE

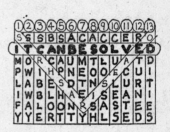

## 60. SCHOOL OF NESSIES

There were only four Nessies – two with no ear flaps and two with both ears.

## 61. SINGLE SUM

```
    107
 + 249
 ─────
    356
```

## 62. SUPER SUM

```
    235
 + 746
 ─────
    981
```

## 63. THE ACTOR NEPHEW

She was Simon's mother.

## 64. ANAGRAMS

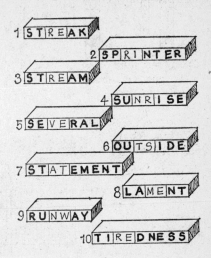

1 STREAK
2 SPRINTER
3 STREAM
4 SUNRISE
5 SEVERAL
6 OUTSIDE
7 STATEMENT
8 LAMENT
9 RUNWAY
10 TIREDNESS

## 65. ONE WORD...

One word.

## 66. SKATEBOARDS

Two, as the problem said.

## 67. THE STRIKING CLOCK

Five seconds. There are three gaps between strikes when the clock sounds 4 o'clock. So each gap takes one second. For 6 o'clock there are five gaps, so it takes five seconds to strike.

## 68. ROUND FIGURES

£0. Rounded off to the nearest £100, £11 is £0.

## 69. STRANGE TO SAY

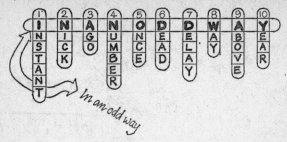

In an odd way

## 70. PATHWAYS PUZZLE
Six ways.

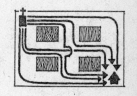

## 71. A-MAZ-ING TOTAL
The smallest possible total is 11.

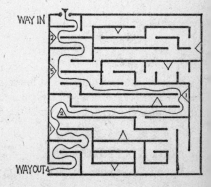

## 72. DO THEY RHYME?

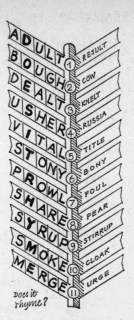

ADULT — ① RESULT
BOUGH — ② COW
DEALT — ③ KNELT
USHER — ④ RUSSIA
VITAL — ⑤ TITLE
STONY — ⑥ BONY
PROWL — ⑦ FOUL
SHARE — ⑧ PEAR
SYRUP — ⑨ STIRRUP
SMOKE — ⑩ CLOAK
MERGE — ⑪ URGE

*Does it rhyme?*

## 73. MAGIC CIRCLES

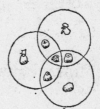

## 74. FOUR FENCES

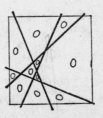

## 75. AS BAD AS ALL THAT?

1. (EXPENSE)
2. (PLACE)
3. (LAST)
4. (WITHOUT)
5. (ACCOUNT)
6. (AGAIN)
7. (LARGE)
8. (FRIEND)
9. (CONTRARY)
10. (DAGGERS)

*Past caring*

## 76. MISSING NUMBERS

A  13 (add 4 each time).
B  64 (double each time).
C  33 (double and take away 1).
D  10 (add 2, then add 1, then 2, then 1, etc.).
E  16 (add 3, then 2, then 3, then 2 . . .).
F  13 (add the previous two figures together—0 + 1 = 1, 1 + 1 = 2, 1 + 2 = 3, etc. This is called the Fibonacci series.)

## 77. BRAINWAVE'S WEIGHING MACHINE
4 kilograms.

## 78. QUICKIE
$50 \div \frac{1}{2} = 100$. Add 2.
Answer: 102.

## 79. FRUIT SQUASH
Cross out 'six letters' and you are left with LEMON.

## 80. OPPOSITES

| | | |
|---|---|---|
| PREVENT | 1 | A L L O W |
| STOP | 2 | B E G I N |
| START | 3 | C E A S E |
| GIANT | 4 | D W A R F |
| LEAVE | 5 | E N T E R |
| TRUE | 6 | F A L S E |
| TAKES | 7 | G I V E S |
| FLAT | 8 | H I L L Y |
| OUTER | 9 | I N N E R |
| SMOOTH | 10 | J E R K Y |
| UNKNOWN | 11 | K N O W N |
| HEAVY | 12 | L I G H T |
| SPENDTHRIFT | 13 | M I S E R |
| QUIET | 14 | N O I S Y |
| INNER | 15 | O U T E R |
| SLIM | 16 | P L U M P |
| SLOW | 17 | Q U I C K |
| COMMONER | 18 | R A R E R |
| DRUNK | 19 | S O B E R |
| LOOSE | 20 | T I G H T |

## 81. WATER, GAS AND ELECTRICITY

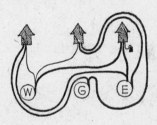

## 82. A CROSS-NUMBER PUZZLE

7 down is $14 \times 14$.

## 83. AMUSED?

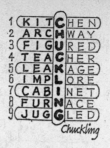

1. (KIT**C**HEN)
2. ARC**H**WAY
3. (FIG**U**RED)
4. TEA**C**HER
5. (LEA**K**AGE)
6. IMP**L**ORE
7. (CAB**I**NET)
8. FUR**N**ACE
9. (JUG**G**LED)

*Chuckling*

## 84. THE FOUR FIVES

$(5 + 5) \times (5 + 5) = 10 \times 10 = 100$

## 85. THE FOUR NINES

$99 + \dfrac{9}{9}$

## 86. THE TWO SEVENS

$$\frac{7}{0.7} = \frac{7}{\dfrac{7}{10}}$$

$$= \frac{70}{7}$$

$$= 10$$

## 87. SHE ONLY SAID 'NO'

She couldn't say a thing to be truthful and logical. For if she said 'No' she was denying she only said 'No' – which was untrue; if she said 'Yes' she was rightly agreeing she only said 'No' but she would have broken her rule of only saying 'No'.

## 88. STRANGERS IN OUR MIDST

1. PAR**S**NIP
2. TAN**T**RUM
3. BAR**R**AGE
4. CAR**A**VAN
5. FUR**N**ACE
6. HAG**G**LED
7. FOR**E**ARM
8. WAR**R**ANT
9. CAP**S**TAN

*Strangers*

## 89. DICE WITH NUMBERS

There are two 'patterned' ways of making up the numbers:
As you see, each comes to 231. So does any other set of figures you
can make.

|     |     |
|-----|-----|
| 61  | 66  |
| 52  | 55  |
| 43  | 44  |
| 34  | 33  |
| 25  | 22  |
| 16  | 11  |
| 231 | 231 |

The sum is bound to be the same in every case, as you always have
the same numbers, 1 to 6 – though in a different order – in both
columns.

## 90. FORCE NEEDED

1. A**P**PEAR
2. AL**P**HAS
3. RE**M**ARK
4. F**A**STEN
5. A**S**CEND
6. H**E**ALED
7. S**P**LASH
8. SU**D**DEN
9. A**S**TRAY
10. S**H**RILL
11. T**H**AWED
12. S**A**VAGE
13. P**R**OFIT
14. A**D**VICE

*Please push hard*

## 91. THE TEA-TABLE FOURSOME

*Method*: A is fixed.

First put B on his right, then swap C and D round – giving two ways; then put C on his right – another two ways; D on his right gives another two ways. Six ways in all.

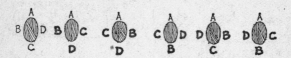

## 92. TANGLE OF TRIANGLES

Sixteen.

## 93. LITTLE IN BIG

① ACCL AIM
② AGIT ATE
③ ALLO WED
④ ANAG RAM
⑤ ANOT HER
⑥ ATTR ACT
⑦ BECA USE
⑧ BENE FIT
⑨ CARA VAN
⑩ PRET END

## 94. BRAINWAVELETS

Jeremy was twelve years old, Sarah ten.

## 95. EXPLORATION CRACKPOT

Nine hundred miles. The easiest way to see it is as a table of gallons left:

|         | 0 miles | 100 | 200 | 300 | 400 | 500 | 600 | 700 | 800 | 900 miles |
|---------|---------|-----|-----|-----|-----|-----|-----|-----|-----|-----------|
| Prof.   | 5 gals  | 4   | 3   | 2   | 1   | 4   | 3   | 2   | 1   | 0 STOP    |
| robot 1 | 5 gals  | 4   | 3   | 2   | 1   |     |     |     |     |           |
| robot 2 | 5 gals  | 4   | 3   | 2   | 1   |     | STOP |    |     |           |
| robot 3 | 5 gals  | 4   | 3   | 2   | 1   |     |     |     |     |           |
| robot 4 | 5 gals  | 4   | 3   | 2   | 1   |     |     |     |     |           |

After 400 miles each buggy has one gallon of fuel left. The Prof. syphons off one gallon from each of the robots to fill his buggy's tank full. He then has five gallons in the tank which will take him a further 500 miles making 900 miles in all.

## 96. THE LONE LITRE

First he filled the three-litre can from the river and tipped it into the five-litre can. Then he refilled the three-litre can. He filled the 5-litre can to the brim, using two of the three litres and leaving exactly one litre in the three-litre can.

## 97. DOWN THE LADDER

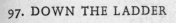

FOOL
FOOT
BOOT
BOAT
GOAT
GOAL
COAL
COAX

## 98. THE PLOT OF GRASS

You can enclose even more land by changing the angle between the two lines which touch one tree only. Try it.

## 99. THE LEAPING FROGS

|  |  | J | K | L |  |
|---|---|---|---|---|---|
| Begin |  |  |  |  |  |
| 1 | K | J |  | L |  |
| 2 | K | J | L |  |  |
| 3 | K |  | L |  | J |
| 4 | K | L |  |  | J |
| 5 |  | L | K | J | End |

## 100. THEY RHYME

FRAIL 1
STALE 2

CHAIR 3
STARE 4

SPEAR 5
STEER 6

LOYAL 7
SPOIL 8

BEARD 9
WEIRD 10

SERVE 11
CURVE 12

PLEAD 13
CREED 14

BUOYS 15
NOISE 16

BUILT 17
SPILT 18

FIELD 19
YIELD 20

## 101. SHARP-SHOOTING
Two shots in the 25 ring, two shots in the 20 ring and two shots in the 3 ring.

## 102. MONTHS OF THE YEAR
All twelve.

## 103. HALF THE AREA
Moving the four matches as shown nips off three squares in the

bottom right corner. So that must leave 6 − 3 or an area of three squares shut in by the newly formed shape.

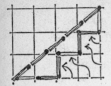

## 104. SHIFTY EYED

No. Cover above and below the eyes and you will see that they are identical.

## 105. CONUNDRUMS

1. Because he makes a little go a long way.
2. Yes, with an egg whisk.
3. Because it wasn't raining.
4. Because we can't get them for nothing.
5. Because it is matchless.
6. A collection of fifty pairs of trousers.
7. In the dark.
8. One is hard to get up and the other is hard to get down.
9. Meet you at the corner.
10. Because she laughed it off.

## 106. DEUCED DICE

Six different doubles − double 1, double 2, etc.

## 107. SALES STUNT

You reduce the price by 10% (a tenth) and then add it on again as a tenth of the price. It's all a matter of the difference between of and off.

## 108. TRICKY TUSK

They are both the same length.

## 109. LOOK, NO REMAINDER!

The trick depends upon a well-known test for dividing by 9; find the sum of the digits of the number and if the sum is divisible by 9 then so is the number. For example, 945: The sum 9 + 4 + 5 = 18, which is divisible by 9. So 945 is, too.

No matter what order the digits are in, the sum of the digits 1 to 9 is 45, which is divisible by 9.

The answer to our division was 53,183,577, no remainder.

## 110. A NUMBER JIG

| 2 | 3 | 4 | 5 | 6 | |
|---|---|---|---|---|---|
| 3 | | | 8 | 1 | 8 | 8 |
| 4 | 4 | 0 | 0 | | 9 | |
| | 0 | | | 1 | 2 |
| 2 | 7 | 5 | 5 | 9 | | 2 |
| 7 | | | | 9 | | 2 |
| 5 | 1 | 0 | 2 | 3 | | 0 |

## 111. TEST YOUR WORD POWER

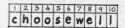

| 1 | 2 | 3 | 4 | 5 | 6 | 7 | 8 | 9 | 10 |
|---|---|---|---|---|---|---|---|---|----|
| c | h | o | o | s | e | w | e | l | l |

## 112. LOOPY SUMS

## 113. CATHERINE WHEEL

Eight spaces.

## 114. THE HOPPING RABBITS

Move the rabbits in the following order:

| Begin | | 1 | 2 | 3 | 4 |
|---|---|---|---|---|---|
| Move 1 | 2 | 1 | | 3 | 4 |
| 2 | 2 | 1 | 4 | 3 | |
| 3 | 2 | 1 | 4 | | 3 |
| 4 | 2 | | 4 | 1 | 3 |
| 5 | | 2 | 4 | 1 | 3 |
| 6 | 4 | 2 | | 1 | 3 |
| 7 | 4 | 2 | 3 | 1 | |
| 8 | 4 | 2 | 3 | | 1 |
| 9 | 4 | | 3 | 2 | 1 |
| 10 | | 4 | 3 | 2 | 1 |

## 115. ANAGRAMS PLUS

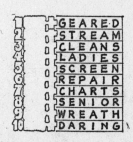

## 116. HALF FULL OR HALF EMPTY?

Professor Brainwave only had to tip his glass so the wine was just about to pour out. Then, if the glass was half full, the wine would just cover the round bottom of the glass. The air above it takes up the other half of the glass.

## 117. THE HATS MIX-UP

Two ways.
Write capital G, B, W for Mr Green, Mr Brown and Mr White. Then use small letters g, b, w for their hats.
Match this in every way. Tick the ways no man gets his hat; put a cross when even one man gets his own hat.

| Men | Hats | | | | | |
|---|---|---|---|---|---|---|
| Mr G | g | g | b | b | w | w |
| Mr B | b | w | g | w | g | b |
| Mr W | w | b | w | g | b | g |
| | x | x | x | ✓ | ✓ | x |

| 13 | 1 | 6 | 10 |
|----|---|---|----|
| 14 | 2 | 5 | 9 |
| ■ | 12 | 11 | 7 |
| 3 | 15 | 8 | 4 |

## 119. WORD ENDINGS

1 I M P **A C T**
2 L A T **H E R**
3 B U T **T O N**
4 F A S **T E N**
5 A S L **A N T**
6 B E L **F R Y**
7 S P L **A S H**
8 S U D **D E N**
9 A S T **R A Y**
10 S H R **I L L**
11 S A V **A G E**
12 P R I **S O N**
13 N A R **R O W**
14 A D D **L E D**
15 S H A **R E D**

## 121. THE THREE JOBS

Winter has a sister so cannot be the head lad, who is an only child.
As Miles earns more than the jockey he cannot be the jockey, nor can
he be the head lad (who earns least). The table looks like this now.
Which shows that Miles can only be the trainer (✓ in the 'Miles'
row) and Smythe is the head lad (✓ at top of 'head lad'
column). Winter is then the jockey.

|  | TRAINER | JOCKEY | HEAD LAD |
|--------|---------|--------|----------|
| SMYTHE |  |  |  |
| MILES |  | X | X |
| WINTER |  |  | X |

## 122. ADD A WORD TO MAKE A WORD

| | | | | | | | |
|---|---|---|---|---|---|---|---|
| 1 | H U M | B L E | | | | | |
| 2 | E A R | L Y | | | | | |
| 3 | R E D | U C E | | | | | |
| 4 | B A N | D A G E | | | | | |
| 5 | A R T | F U L | | | | | |
| 6 | G O T | H I C | | | | | |
| 7 | G I N | G E R | | | | | |
| 8 | A D D | L E | | | | | |
| 9 | G E T | A W A Y | | | | | |
| 10 | E N D | A N G E R | | | | | |

Her baggage

## 123. RAISE YOUR GLASSES

The lenses all have the same curves, arcs of similar circles. So they all curve the same. So they could all belong to Brainwave or all belong to Crackpot.

## 124. THE QUARRELSOME NEIGHBOURS

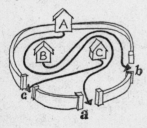

## 125. FAIR SQUARES

Use both sides of the ruler! First lay the ruler along each of the edges at the corner of the page and draw lines on the other side of the ruler. Then move the ruler in and draw a second pair of lines.

You will then have a square having sides equal to the ruler's width. (The square will be one ruler's width in from the edge of the page.)

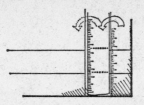

## 126. IN A NEW GUISE

1. C A R E S
2. S L U M P
3. F L O G
4. L A N E
5. A N T L E R
6. C A N O E
7. A G R E E S
8. G R O U S E
9. G A R D E N
10. S M U G
11. A S C E N D

*All anagrams*

## 128. CHINESE PLATE-SPINNER

No. The pole is as long as the plate is wide.

## 129. POTTY PROVERB

People who live in grass houses *shouldn't stow thrones.*

## 130. DE-COMPOSITION

A. Handel
B. Schumann
C. Bach
D. Offenbach
E. Haydn
F. Chopin

## 131. DOMINO FRACTIONS

$\frac{3}{4} + \frac{1}{4} = 1$

$\frac{3}{6} + \frac{1}{2} = \frac{1}{2} + \frac{1}{2} = 1$

$\frac{1}{2} + \frac{3}{6} + \frac{3}{4} + \frac{1}{4} = 2$

$1 + 1 = 2$

## 132. PROBLEM PICTURE

Four elephants sniffing a hot cross bun

## 133. CHEERIO!

1. AMICABLE
2. UNASHAMED
3. PARALLEL
4. HOUSEHOLD
5. DEXTERITY
6. BANDANNA
7. IRONICAL
8. HERALDRY
9. FLORIDLY
10. KNOCKOUT